BOOK ONE
Lessons 1-24

MASTER METHOD
FOR BAND

A Fundamental Class Instruction Book
for all Band Instruments

— 24 LESSONS —

155 Exercises

82 Familiar Melodies

44 Special Rhythm Drills

40 Duets and Trios

by

CHARLES S. PETERS

Paul Yoder, Editor

INSTRUMENTATION

C Flute - Piccolo [34FL]	B♭ Soprano Saxophone [34XB]	Baritone T.C. [34TC]
E♭ Clarinet [34CLE]	E♭ Alto Saxophone [34XE]	Baritone B.C. [34BC]
B♭ Clarinet [34CL]	B♭ Tenor Saxophone [34XB]	Trombone [34TB]
Alto Clarinet [34CLE]	E♭ Baritone Saxophone [34XE]	Basses (E♭ & BB♭) [34BS]
B♭ Bass Clarinet [34CLB]	B♭ Cornet - Trumpet [34TP]	Drums [34DR]
Bassoon [34BN]	E♭ Alto (Mellophone) [34ME]	
Oboe [34OB]	F Horn [34HF]	

Conductor--Full Score and Manual [34F]

© MCMLVIII NEIL A. KJOS MUSIC CO., Publisher. Park Ridge. Ill.

ISBN 0-8497-0001-9

International Copyright Secured

TO THE STUDENT
Study this page carefully

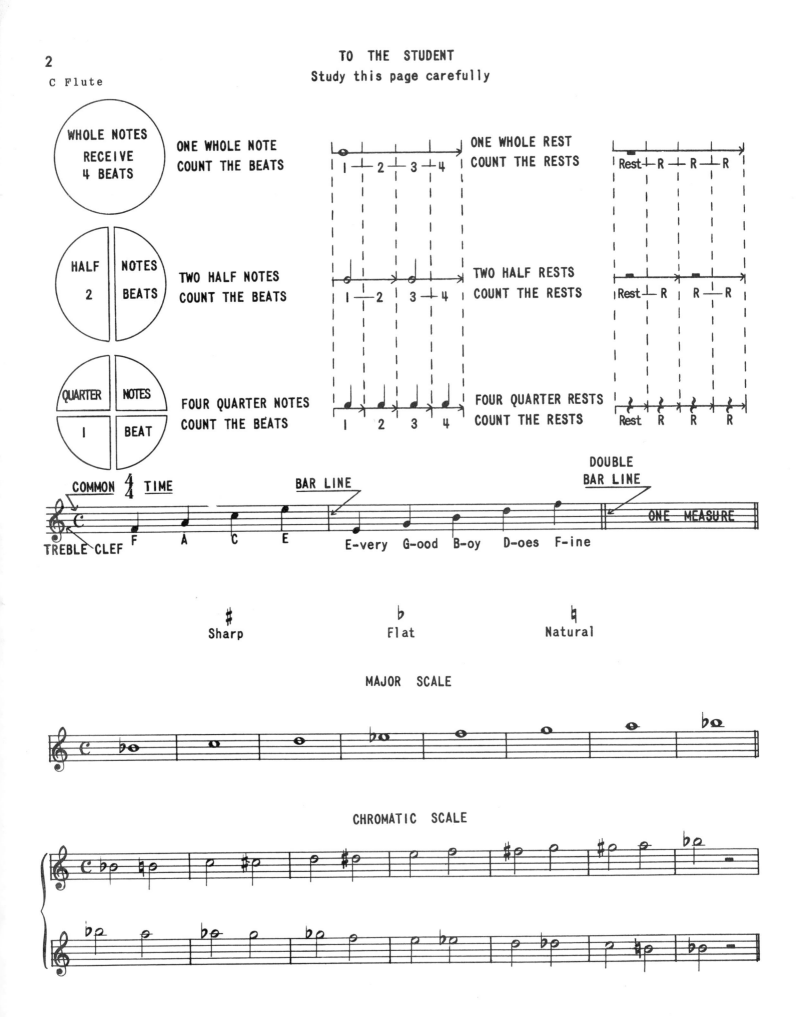

LESSON 1

C Flute

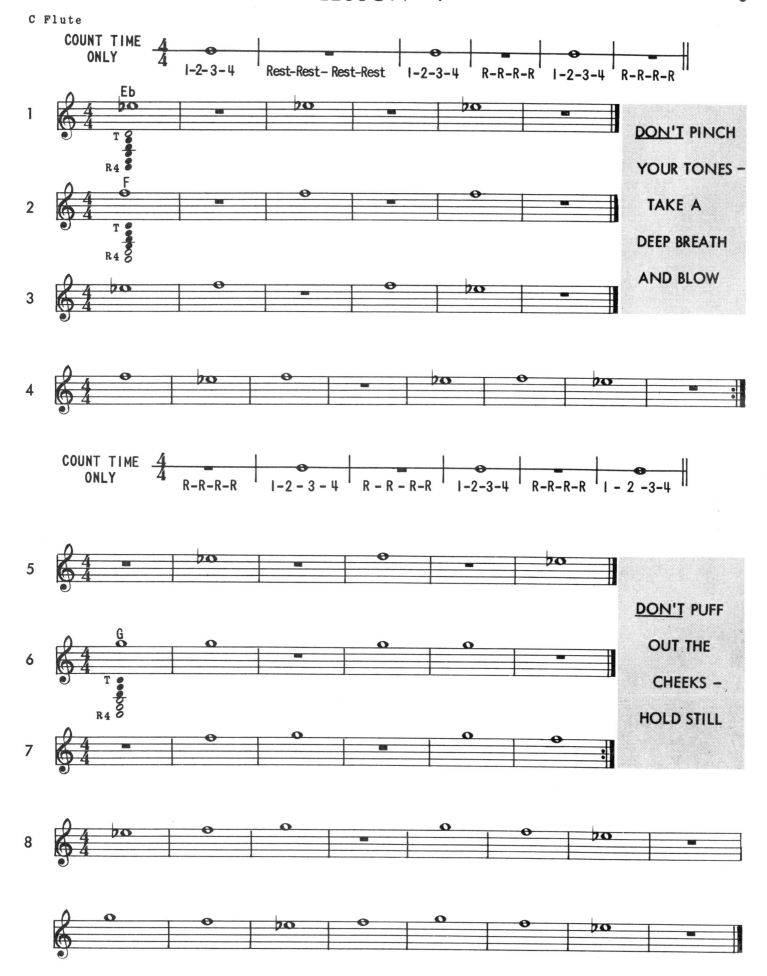

LESSON 2

COUNT TIME ONLY

DON'T RAISE
YOUR
SHOULDER
OR PUSH OUT
YOUR CHEST
WHEN
BREATHING

DON'T MOVE
UP AND DOWN
AND
ALL AROUND—
SIT STILL

LESSON 3

C Flute

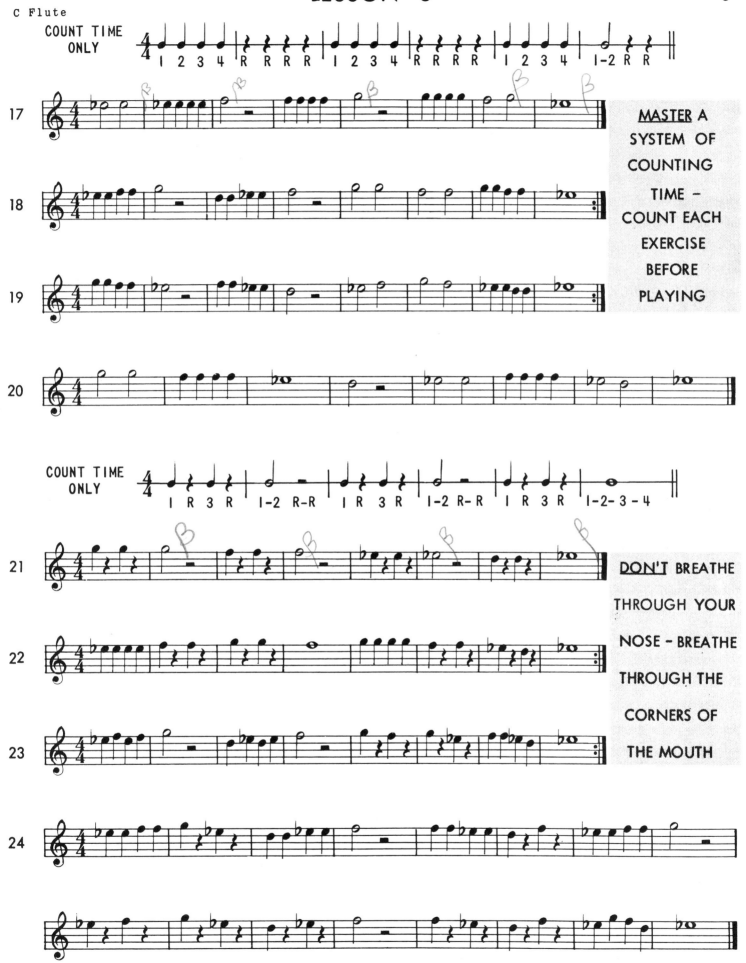

MASTER A
SYSTEM OF
COUNTING
TIME –
COUNT EACH
EXERCISE
BEFORE
PLAYING

DON'T BREATHE
THROUGH YOUR
NOSE – BREATHE
THROUGH THE
CORNERS OF
THE MOUTH

LESSON 4

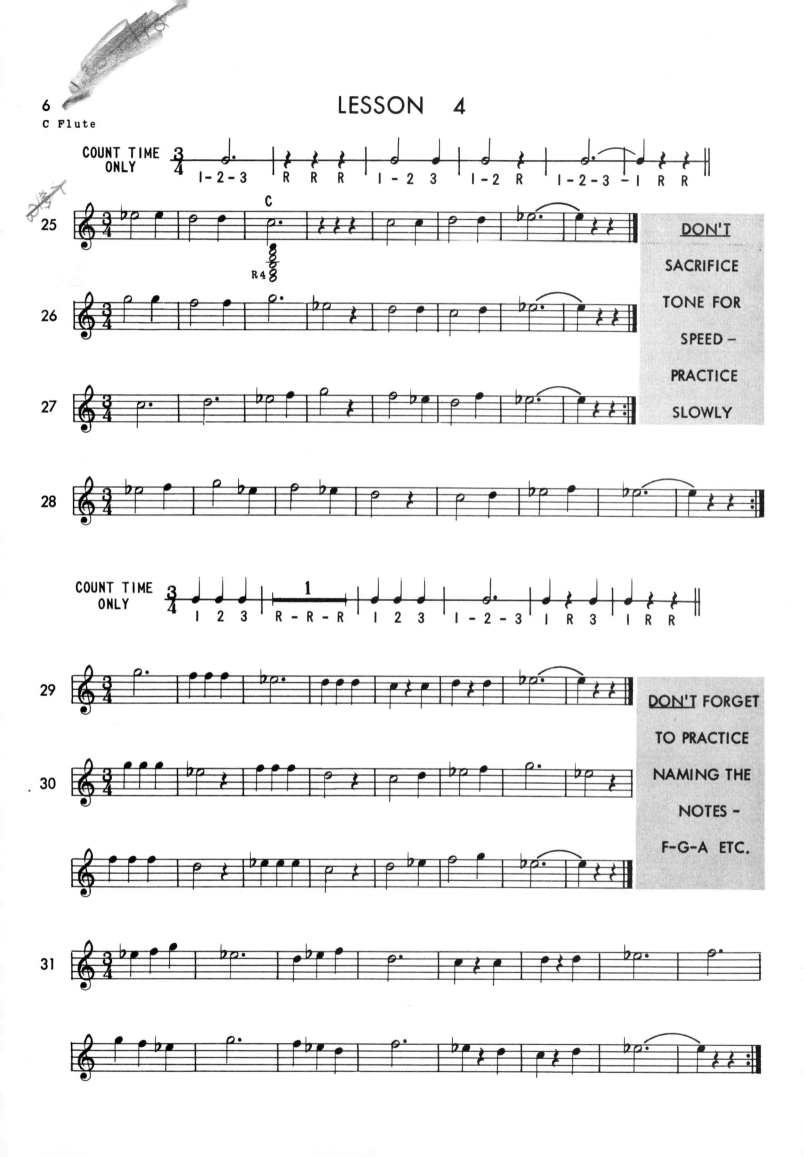

1st Part   Merrily We Roll Along

2nd Part

1st Part   Same tune in different rhythm

2nd Part

1st Part   At Pierrot's Door

2nd Part

1st Part   Indian Dance

2nd Part

LESSON 6

LESSON 7

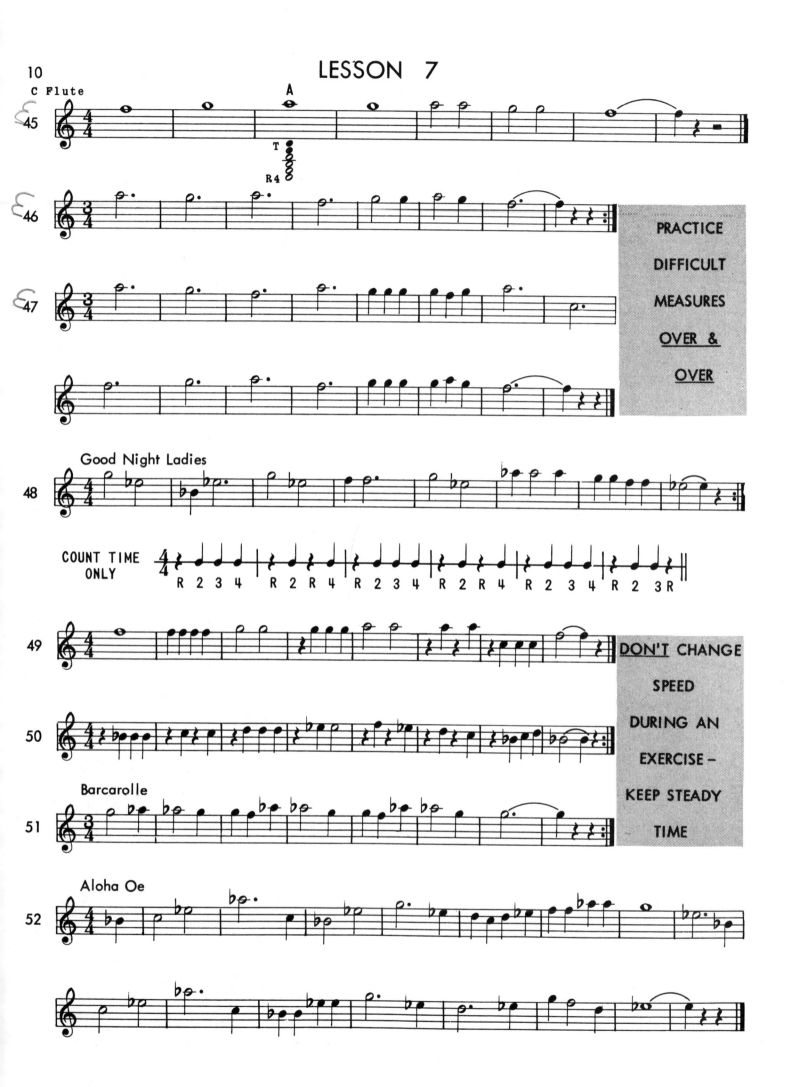

C Flute

45

46

47

PRACTICE

DIFFICULT

MEASURES

OVER &

OVER

Good Night Ladies

48

COUNT TIME
ONLY

49

DON'T CHANGE

SPEED

DURING AN

EXERCISE –

KEEP STEADY

TIME

50

Barcarolle

51

Aloha Oe

52

LESSON 8

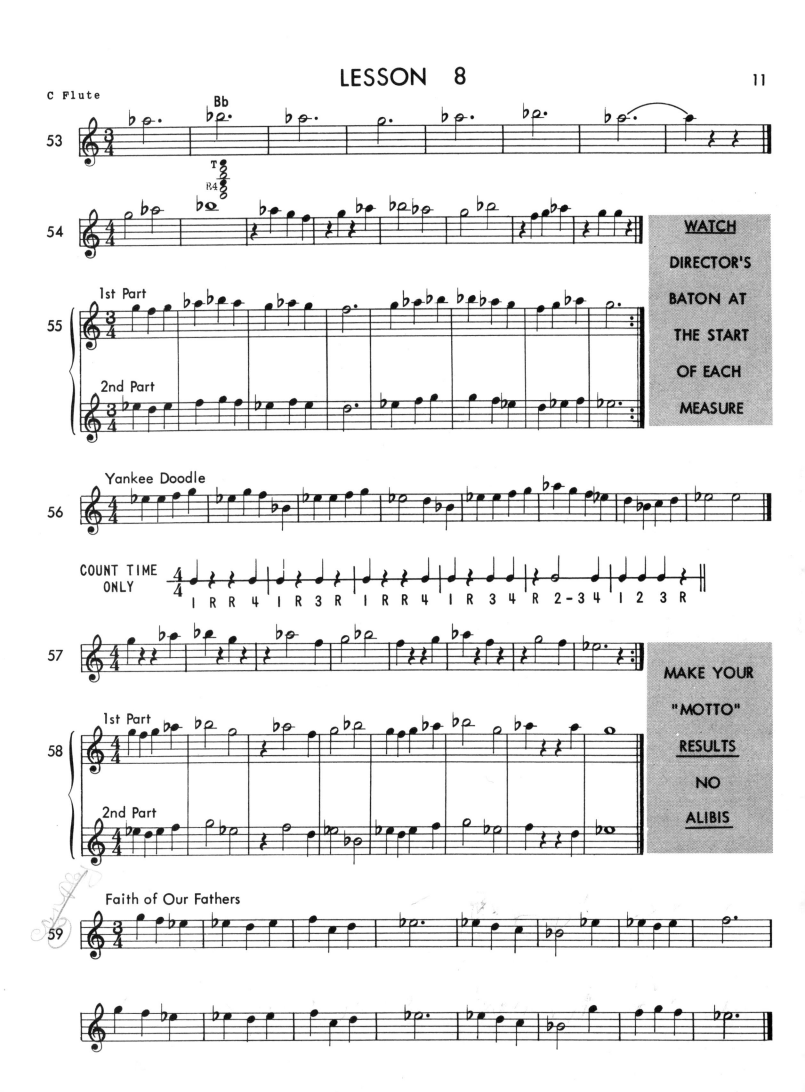

WATCH
DIRECTOR'S
BATON AT
THE START
OF EACH
MEASURE

MAKE YOUR
"MOTTO"
RESULTS
NO
ALIBIS

SOLOS & DUETS

LESSON 9

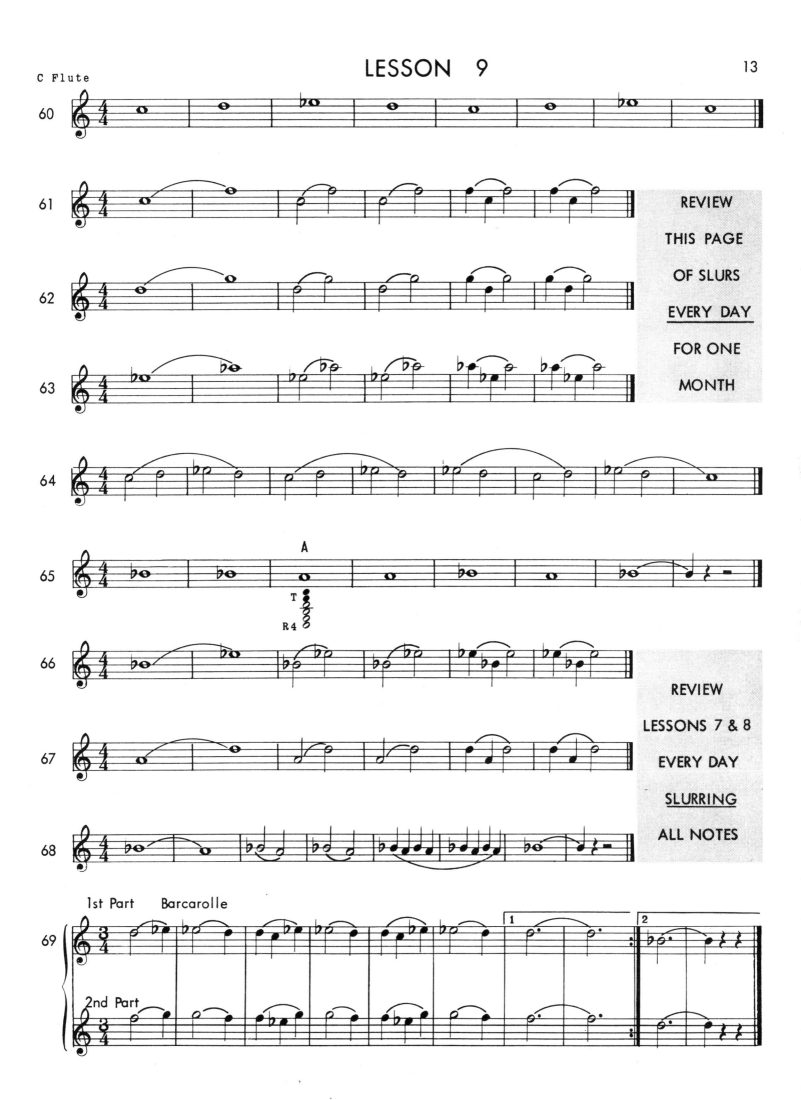

REVIEW
THIS PAGE
OF SLURS
EVERY DAY
FOR ONE
MONTH

REVIEW
LESSONS 7 & 8
EVERY DAY
SLURRING
ALL NOTES

LESSON 10

C Flute

COUNT TIME ONLY
1 2   1 — 2   1 - 2 - 1 R   1 2   1 - 2   1 - 2 - 1 R

70

MEMORIZE

THE SCALE

IN EXERCISE

NUMBER 70

FORWARDS AND

BACKWARDS

Long, Long Ago

71

72

COUNT TIME ONLY
1 an 2 an   1   2   1 an 2 an   1   2   1 an 2 an   1 - 2

73

PRACTICE

ALL EXERCISES

THREE SPEEDS

- SLOW

74

- MEDIUM

- FAST

1st Part   Jolly Old St. Nick

75

2nd Part

LESSON 12

C Flute

PRACTICE
ALL DUETS
(AND EXERCISES)
WITH FRIENDS
INVITE THEM
TO YOUR
HOME

MEMORIZE
THE SCALE
IN EXERCISE
NUMBER 86
FORWARDS AND
BACKWARDS

SOLOS - DUETS - TRIOS

LESSON 13

C Flute

MEMORIZE
THE SCALE IN
EXERCISE 88 –
STUDY
KEY SIGNATURE
IN EXERCISE 89

Auld Lang Syne

"D.S. AL FINE"
MEANS TO
REPEAT FROM
THE SIGN 𝄋
TO THE
END (FINE)

Amici

Fine

D.S. al Fine

LESSON 14

LESSON 15

C Flute

C Flute

LESSON 16

C Flute

COUNT TIME ONLY

1st Part Chopsticks

2nd Part

PRACTICE WITH

A METRONOME

SLOW FIRST

THEN FASTER

ONE NOTCH

AT A TIME

Drink to Me Only with Thine Eyes

COUNT TIME ONLY

CORRECT

USE OF THE

FINGER TIPS

WILL INCREASE

YOUR

TECHNIC

1st Part

2nd Part

When Johnny Comes Marching Home

LESSON 18

LESSON 19

COUNT TIME
ONLY

I - 2   I   2   I an 2 an   I   2 an I - 2 - I R R

123

Ȼ IS CALLED:

1. ALLA BREVE

2. CUT TIME

3. MARCH TIME

STUDY

THE COUNTING

CAREFULLY

Salut d'amour

124

R4

Bugle Call

125

COUNT TIME
ONLY

I - 2 an   I - 2 an   I an-2 an   I an-2 an   I an 2   I - 2 R

126

F#

T

R4

INSTRUMENTS

IN GOOD

CONDITION

ARE EASY

TO BLOW

WHEN CORRECTLY

PLAYED

Hot Time in the Old Town

127

1st Part   When the Work's All Done This Fall

128

2nd Part

LESSON 20

LESSON 21

C Flute

LESSON 22

Listen to the Mocking Bird

LESSON 23

C FLUTE

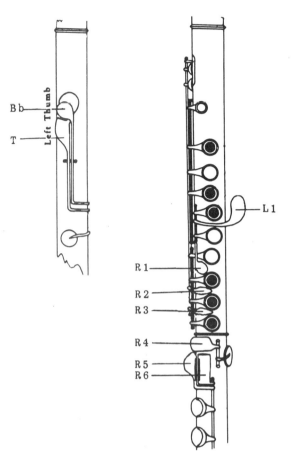

Music for the C Flute is written in Treble Clef and sounds as written.

FINGERING CHART

The black dots indicate closed tone holes, and the open circles indicate open tone holes. The letters and numerals indicate that the corresponding key should be pressed (See diagram of instrument for letter and numbered names of keys).

CONCERT PITCH	c	c# db	d	d# eb	e	f	f# gb	g	g# a	a	a# bb	b
C FLUTE	C	C#Db	D	D#Eb	E	F	F#Gb	G	G#Ab	A	A#Bb	B